1909   1929

Taft, Wilson, Harding, & Coolidge

ROURKE'S COMPLETE HISTORY OF OUR PRESIDENTS ENCYCLOPEDIA

Volume 8

Kelli L. Hicks, Editor

Ypsilanti District Library
5577 Whittaker Road
Ypsilanti, MI 48197

Rourke Publishing

Vero Beach, Florida 32964 | www.rourkepublishing.com

© 2009 Rourke Publishing LLC

All rights reserved. No part of this book may be reproduced or utilized in any form or by any means, electronic or mechanical including photocopying, recording, or by any information storage and retrieval system without permission in writing from the publisher.

www.rourkepublishing.com

PHOTO CREDITS: Pages 4, 5, 6, 7, 8, 9, 10, 11, 12, 13, 14, 15, 16, 17, 18, 19, 20, 21, 22, 26, 27, 28, 29, 30, 31, 32, 33, 34, 36, 38, 39, 40, 41, 42, 43, 44, 45, 46, 47, 48, 49, 50, 51, 52, 53 © Library of Congress

Editor: Kelli L. Hicks

Cover and interior design by Nicola Stratford, bdpublishing.com

Library of Congress Cataloging-in-Publication Data

Rourke's Complete History of Our Presidents Encyclopedia / Kelli L. Hicks
 p. cm.
 Includes bibliographical references and index.
 Summary: Discusses the political lives and times of the men who served as United States presidents, their administrations, and the events which occurred during their tenures.
 Set ISBN 978-1-60694-293-2
 Title ISBN 978-1-60694-301-4
 1. Presidents—United States—Juvenile literature.

Printed in the USA

CG/CG

www.rourkepublishing.com – rourke@rourkepublishing.com
Post Office Box 3328, Vero Beach, FL 32964

America Comes of Age 4

William H. Taft (1909-1913) 10

Woodrow Wilson (1913-1921) 18

Warren Harding (1921-1923) 32

Calvin Coolidge (1923-1929) 40

The Presidency in War and Peace 48

Cabinet Members 54

Timeline 56

Presidents of the United States 60

Index 62

Further Reading 64

4 America Comes of Age

America Comes of Age

During the early 1900s, America seemed to be a nation that would enjoy peace and prosperity forever. Theodore Roosevelt, one of the country's most popular leaders, presided over the White House. Youthful and exuberant, he attacked big-industry monopolies and their unfair trade practices. He sent navy ships around the world to visit America's new overseas territories and to display American power. One of the country's first environmentalists, he eagerly set aside thousands of square miles of land as part of America's new national park system.

When Roosevelt left the White House in 1909, he turned the presidency over to his handpicked successor and close friend, William Howard Taft.

Theodore Roosevelt raised a volunteer group of soldiers called the Rough Riders who fought the Spanish in Cuba in 1898.

William Howard Taft, wearing crown, seated on shoulder of Theodore Roosevelt.

The country is in safe hands while Theodore Roosevelt is at the helm.

America Comes of Age

Roosevelt and Taft, however, soon began to quarrel. Roosevelt believed that Taft was too conservative and betrayed the policies for which Roosevelt had fought so hard. Their fight divided the Republican Party. In 1912, Taft received a renomination for a second term, and Roosevelt decided to run for president on a third-party ticket. When Roosevelt said that he felt as vigorous as a bull moose, his party received the title of the Bull Moose Party.

Woodrow Wilson

Peace and War

Because the Republican vote split between Roosevelt and Taft, the Democrats won the 1912 presidential election. In March 1913, Woodrow Wilson, a former college professor, became president of the United States. His eight years in office proved to be one of the most significant periods of change in U.S. history.

President Wilson enacted many of the reforms that Roosevelt had supported. He established the Federal Reserve, which was a national banking system. He also passed other measures to break up monopolies in order to guarantee the right of competition in American business.

However, Wilson became increasingly preoccupied with America's role in foreign affairs. In 1914, Europe was plunged into a great war, World War I. The people of the United States wanted to stay out of the war, and Wilson did attempt to keep the nation from being involved.

But German submarines were attacking American ships, which were bringing goods and weapons to Great Britain. The German attacks angered the nation, and by 1917, President Wilson felt that he had no other choice but to go to war. In April of that year, the U.S. Congress, at the request of the president, declared war against Germany.

Words to Know

Bull Moose Party (BUL MOOSS PAR-tee): A third party, officially called the Progressive Party, founded in 1912 by former president Theodore Roosevelt and other Insurgent Republicans.

America Comes of Age

World War I

World War I brought about major changes in American life. The draft raised an army of 4 million men. More than 2 million of them received orders to go to France to fight with the other allied powers (Great Britain, the Soviet Union, and France) against Germany.

At home, women worked in factories and volunteered as nurses to help in the war effort. Another great change was the movement of African Americans from the South to the cities of the North in search of work and a better life. People across the land lived on rations for the duration of the war.

A soldier holds up a U.S. flag during World War I.

8 America Comes of Age

Women and Voting

One movement that would have a major impact on life and politics in the 1900s was the women's suffrage, or the movement to obtain the right to vote for women. Groups pushing for the right of all women in the United States to vote formed in the previous century. Until the 1890s, prominent women such as Elizabeth Cady Stanton led them. She believed that educated women would best promote women's influence in public life.

Other women, however, believed that women's rights were much broader than simply the right to vote. One of these was Harriet Stanton Blatch, Cady Stanton's own daughter. Blatch wanted the fight for women's rights to touch on economic issues as well. She believed that women should receive equal pay to men for their work and that suffrage would be valuable because it would give all women influence in society.

There was always a division in the suffrage movement between middle and upper-class women on the one hand and poor working women on the other. By 1912, nine states in the West had granted women the right to vote. These modest successes pushed women to press for a constitutional amendment granting all women the right to vote. In the years after 1912, women picketed and protested and advertised their cause in newspapers and magazines.

The final victory, the passage of the Nineteenth Amendment in 1919, came about largely because of the heroic work of American women from 1917 to 1918, during World War I. Legislators realized that they could no longer deny women their basic right to vote after having served as nurses, medical volunteers, and factory workers during the conflict.

The first group of suffrage supporters take part in a political campaign in 1914.

America Comes of Age

In addition, certain civil liberties were restricted during the conflict. For example, an arrest for treason was liable for anyone attacking such institutions as the draft. This was a clear violation of the right of free speech.

The Roaring Twenties

When the war ended in 1918, the American people wanted nothing more than to return to their prewar happiness. During the election year of 1920, the Republican presidential candidate, Warren Harding, called for a return to normalcy, meaning the way things had been.

But the 1920s would not be a return to the good old days; they would be a period of dramatic social change. American families acquired radios and automobiles on a wide scale. Women's skirts became shorter; a dramatic change from the floor length dresses common throughout all of American history.

A period known as Prohibition made the sale of alcohol illegal throughout the nation during the 1920s. Liquor was available in underground saloons called speakeasies. They received this name because a secret code word was required to gain admittance. Very few people paid any attention to the law.

While these and other striking changes were occurring in society during the 1920s, a series of bland and relatively weak presidents sat in the White House. Warren Harding died in office in 1923 and Calvin Coolidge became his successor. He was a man who said, and did little. The action seemed to be not in the White House but in the private sectors of business and entertainment. The presidency, for the time being, would play a smaller role in American life.

World War 1 brought great changes to the lives of women; many worked outside the home for the first time.

Words to Know

normalcy (NOR-muhl-see): A term coined by Warren Harding in 1920 and meaning "the state of being normal." Although grammatically incorrect at the time, it has since become a recognized word in the English language.

William H. Taft

William Howard Taft began his service in government when he was 24 years old. By the time he was in his late forties, he was a member of President Theodore Roosevelt's cabinet and a close personal friend of the president's. He was such a trusted friend to Roosevelt that the president handpicked Taft to be his successor. But Taft's term as president was an unhappy one. It was marked by an end to his friendship with Roosevelt, the splitting of his political party, and the overwhelming rejection by American voters in his bid for reelection in 1912.

In 1921, eight years after leaving the White House, Taft achieved the position he had always really wanted, that of chief justice of the United States Supreme Court. William Howard Taft thus became the only person to hold both the highest office in the executive branch and the highest office in the judicial branch.

Vice President James S. Sherman

William H. Taft

Born:
September 15, 1857
Cincinnati, OH

Ohio

Term:
March 4, 1909 – March 4, 1913

Party:
Republican

First Lady:
Helen Herron Taft

Vice President:
James S. Sherman

Died:
March 8, 1930
Washington, D.C.

William H. Taft

27th President of the United States

Early Life and Political Career

William Howard Taft was born in Cincinnati, Ohio, on September 15, 1857. A large baby, he was affectionately known as Big Lub, and he remained large all his life. By the time he became president, Taft, who stood 6 feet 2 inches, weighed more than 300 pounds.

His father, Alphonso Taft, was a lawyer and judge who had served in President Ulysses S. Grant's Cabinet and as a foreign minister during President Chester Arthur's administration. Taft's mother, Louisa Torrey Taft, was Alphonso's second wife. In addition to William, the couple had three other children.

William entered Yale University in 1874. He graduated second in his class in 1878 and returned to Cincinnati to attend law school. Taft earned his law degree in 1880.

The Taft family was prosperous and well known in Cincinnati, and young William was soon able to get an appointment to political office. In 1881, he received the position of assistant prosecuting attorney.

Six years later, at the age of 30, he became a judge in the Cincinnati Superior Court. The year before, in 1886, Taft had married Helen "Nellie" Herron, the daughter of a prominent lawyer. Nellie's father gave the young couple a lot overlooking the Ohio River as a wedding present, and they built a house on the land.

Life for the Tafts was serene and prosperous. At a young age, they had everything anyone could want, including a growing family of three children: Robert Alphonso, Helen, and Charles. But Washington, D.C., and a higher political office, soon called.

President Taft with his family.

William H. Taft

Judge and Governor

In 1890, Taft received an appointment to his first important federal position. He was named solicitor general of the United States. The solicitor general is the principal lawyer for the United States government and argues its cases before the Supreme Court. Taft held this job for two years before receiving an appointment to be a judge of the federal circuit court.

In 1900, President William McKinley asked Taft to leave the federal bench and become president of the Philippine Commission. The United States had acquired the Philippines as a result of the Spanish-American War of 1898.

Taft's job was to form a civilian government in the Philippines, which the U.S. military ruled since 1898. To achieve this end, Taft became governor of the Philippines. He held complete authority to form a civilian government and to create a police force, a judiciary, and a tax system.

Taft became very fond of the people of the Philippines, and they in turn came to trust him and his family. He tried to be fair and made sure that the poorest people received land on which they could start farms. Within two years, he helped to improve economic conditions and had established limited self-government.

William Taft helped create a civilian government in the Philippines. The people trusted his decisions and believed him to be fair.

Secretary of War

Taft's work in the Philippines caused President Theodore Roosevelt to call him back to Washington late in 1903 to become secretary of war. Roosevelt, Taft, and Secretary of State Elihu Root worked so well together that many referred to them as the "Three Musketeers."

On the night of his election in 1904, Roosevelt said that he would not run for president again in 1908. The question for the president then was who would succeed him? Roosevelt felt that Taft was the person to continue his policies.

President Taft

The Republican National Convention was completely under the control of President Roosevelt and they nominated Taft. Senator James S. Sherman received the nomination for vice president. In the November election, Taft easily defeated his Democratic opponent, William Jennings Bryan, with 321 electoral votes to Bryan's 162.

By 1908, however, arguments were beginning to break out within the Republican Party. Republicans from the West, known as Insurgents, clamored for reforms in big business and trusts. They also demanded more social legislation to protect workers and farmers, and they wanted to change the presidential nominating system to include more state primary elections and lessen the influence of the big political bosses.

The more conservative Republicans, known as Stalwarts, were centered in the East. They wanted business to be free of government interference. They were also in favor of high tariffs, taxes on imports, little or no social legislation, and they did not want primary elections.

William H. Taft

Roosevelt had been able to hold the quarreling factions together by the force of his strong personality. But Taft was a less dazzling figure. A hard worker, he was never able to popularize his accomplishments the way Roosevelt had. Moreover, during his early years as president, he had chosen to ignore the growing division between the Insurgents and the Stalwarts.

Words to Know

Insurgents (IN-surj-ents): Liberal Republicans who in 1912 were opposed to many policies of the Taft administration.

Stalwarts (STALL-wurts): Conservative Republicans who were the major backers of President William Taft in 1912.

First Lady Helen Taft

Helen Herron, known as Nellie to her family and friends, was born into a prosperous Ohio family in 1861. She attended private school in Cincinnati. At age 16, Helen went to the White House to visit President and Mrs. Rutherford B. Hayes, who were friends of her father's.

In 1879, she met "that adorable Will Taft" for the first time and discovered that they had many similar interests, including a love of classical music. They were married in 1886 and settled in Cincinnati, where they hoped to raise their family.

Nellie Taft was her husband's biggest supporter, and she believed that he would one day be president. In the early years, however, his career took him from one office to another. In 1900, President William McKinley asked him to move to the Philippines to help form a civilian government in the new American colony.

Helen Herron Taft

Mrs. Taft welcomed the challenge, and even though they had three children, she willingly went with Taft on his new assignment. In Asia, she had the opportunity to travel to China and Japan and undertook a special diplomatic mission to the Vatican.

Nellie Taft urged her husband to run for president in 1908, even though he would have preferred to become a judge again. She stood proudly at his side when he was sworn in as the twenty-seventh president on March 4, 1909. Two months later, she suffered a severe stroke that left her temporarily paralyzed.

She fought the effects of the stroke with determination and on New Year's Eve 1909 was able to make her first public appearance since struck by illness. She never, however, made a full recovery.

The Taft White House was noted for the brilliance of its parties, the most famous being the garden party that was held to celebrate the president and Mrs. Taft's twenty-fifth wedding anniversary in 1911. Several thousand people attended.

One of Mrs. Taft's special projects was the planting of Washington's famous cherry trees, which workers placed around the tidal basin at her request. The Tafts were the last First Couple to have an animal grazing on the White House lawn. Their cow, named Pauline Wayne, roamed the White House grounds and was a source of milk for the First Family.

Nellie Taft's public role in Washington received interruption only temporarily when Taft left the White House in 1913. Eight years later, he became chief justice, and she assumed the social obligation of the wife of the nation's highest judge. She continued to live in Washington after Taft's death in 1930 and died at her home there on May 22, 1943, at the age of 81.

William H. Taft

When he failed to make any appointments of pro-Insurgents to his cabinet, the split widened. In 1909, Congress passed the Payne-Aldrich Tariff, which raised tariff rates on more than 600 items. The Insurgents, who opposed high tariffs, were outraged. The Republican platform of 1908 had called for lower tariffs. By supporting the Payne-Aldrich bill, Taft broke a campaign promise.

Taft also seemed to be less of a conservationist than Roosevelt was. The Insurgents accused Taft's secretary of the interior, Richard Ballinger, of favoring the coal-mining and timber interests over environmental concerns. Ballinger also got into an embarrassing fight with Gifford Pinchot, who received the appointment by Roosevelt to protect and run the national park system. When Taft fired Pinchot, the party divided even further.

By 1910, the Republican Party had so damaged itself that the Democrats won control of the House of Representatives. This was an ominous sigh for Taft's reelection possibilities. Of even greater concern was the fact that Roosevelt was now extremely angry at Taft.

The Bull Moose Election

As soon as Taft became president in March 1909, Theodore Roosevelt left the country to go on a safari in Africa. He hoped to take the spotlight off himself and give Taft breathing room to establish his presidency.

Gifford Pinchot was appointed by Roosevelt to run the national park system.

However, when Roosevelt reached Europe in early 1910, what he heard about Taft alarmed him.

Taft, it seemed, was betraying many of the most important principles that they had worked on together in the early 1900s.

Words to Know

Payne-Aldrich Tariff (PEYN-AWL-drich TA-rif): A tariff passed by Congress in 1909 that dramatically increased rates on many items.

William H. Taft

Roosevelt decided to challenge Taft for the Republican presidential nomination in 1912. The party, however, was now firmly under the control of Taft and his allies, much as it had been under Roosevelt's control in 1908. Despite a vigorous fight, Roosevelt was unable to prevent Taft from receiving an easy renomination.

Roosevelt and his supporters stormed out of the convention and formed a new party, called the Progressive Party. When asked by a reporter how he felt, Roosevelt replied, "as strong as a bull moose." They soon dubbed the new party the Bull Moose Party.

Roosevelt's 1912 campaign split the Republican Party vote, which enabled the Democratic candidate, Woodrow Wilson, to win the presidential election. Taft received only 8 electoral votes, coming in far behind Wilson's 435 electoral votes and Roosevelt's 88 electoral votes. It was a humiliating defeat.

After the White House

Taft was happy to leave the White House on March 4, 1913. Soon afterward, he accepted a position as professor of constitutional law at Yale University. With his career in government seemingly over, Taft became a respected professor and an advocate of arbitration, decision by a third party, to settle world disputes.

In 1920, the Republicans won the White House again, and Warren Harding became president. Much to Taft's surprise, President Harding offered him the position of chief justice of the United States Supreme Court. Thus, at age 64, Taft achieved the position he had longed for all his life.

He served as chief justice until February 3, 1930, when he resigned because of a heart ailment. On March 8 of the same year, he died in Washington, D.C. Taft is buried in Arlington National Cemetery, one of only two presidents to be buried there. The other is John F. Kennedy.

William Taft, Warren Harding, and Robert Lincoln, on May 30, 1922.

Woodrow Wilson

Woodrow Wilson was a Virginia-born college professor who arrived in the White House after serving only two years as governor of New Jersey. A Democrat, he worked diligently during his first year as president to pass some of the most sweeping reform legislation in the country's history.

However, foreign affairs seemed to occupy most of his presidency. First, he tried to keep the United States out of World War I, and then, reluctantly, he led the nation into the conflict in 1917. In his final years as president, he was plagued by ill health and bitter political failures, as Congress refused to ratify the peace treaty that Wilson had helped to negotiate or to join the new world body, the League of Nations.

During this sad time, the president remained in his darkened bedroom while First Lady Edith Wilson carefully screened all visitors and correspondence and, in the eyes of many, ruled the country as its unofficial president.

Vice President Thomas R. Marshall

Woodrow Wilson

Born:
December 28, 1856
Staunton, VA

Virginia — Staunton

Term:
March 4, 1913 - March 4, 1921

Party:
Democratic

First Lady:
Ellen Louise Axson Wilson
Edith Bolling Wilson

Vice President:
Thomas R. Marshall

Died:
February 3, 1924
Washington, D.C.

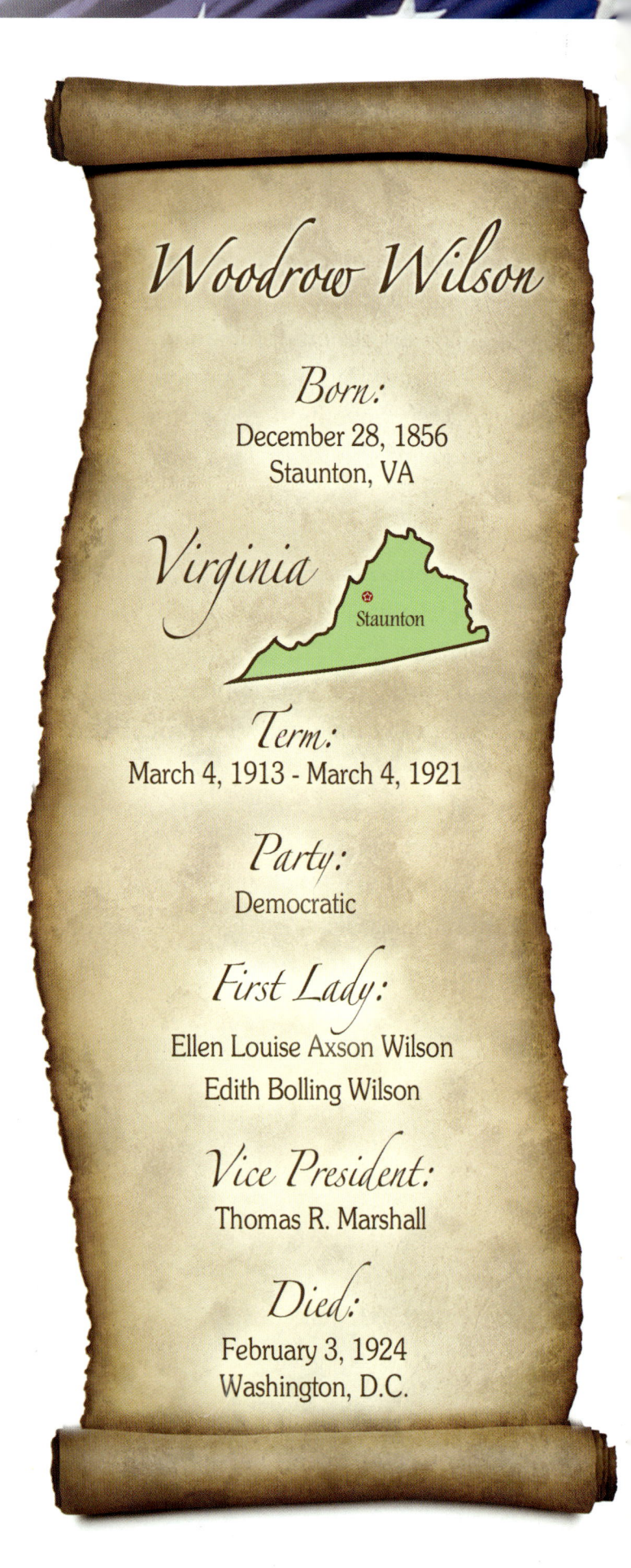

Woodrow Wilson

28th President of the United States

Woodrow Wilson

Early Life

Thomas Woodrow Wilson was born in Staunton, Virginia, on December 28, 1856. His father, Joseph Ruggles Wilson, was a Presbyterian minister. Numerous Presbyterian ministers were also in the family of his mother, Janet Wilson.

When "Tommy" Wilson was a year old, his family moved to Augusta, Georgia. When he was four, he remembered, a neighbor called out that Abraham Lincoln won the election for president and that there would be civil war. Wilson's childhood memories of the destruction wrought by the Civil War remained with him into adulthood and strengthened his desire as president to work for peace.

His father taught young Tommy at home until he was 12 years old. From an early age, he showed a talent for writing and speaking. When the family moved to Columbia, South Carolina, in 1870, Tommy was already reading books about government. After reading a book about a famous British prime minister, young Wilson said to his father, "I intend to be a statesman too."

In 1875, Wilson earned admittance to Princeton University. There, he was active in the debating society and studied public speaking. He graduated in 1879 and went on to study law at the University of Virginia. In 1882, Wilson became a lawyer. In 1883, while on a visit to Georgia, he resumed a friendship with an acquaintance from his childhood, Ellen Louise Axson. He was immediately attracted to Miss Elly Lou, and they were married in 1885.

Woodrow Wilson and his future wife Ellen Louise Axson visit Princeton University.

Wilson soon realized that he did not enjoy the practice of law. He went back to school, to Johns Hopkins University, and in 1886, he received a Ph.D. in political science. His doctoral dissertation, entitled Congressional Government, was published in 1885 and is still considered a classic study of how the U.S. Congress operates.

University Career

After receiving his doctorate, Wilson taught at Bryn Mawr and at Wesleyan University before returning to Princeton in 1890 as a professor of jurisprudence, the science or philosophy of law, and political economy. He was a superb lecturer and was popular with the students. In 1902, he became president of the university.

As president of Princeton, Wilson instituted a number of educational reforms. He strove to raise academic standards, reorganized the curriculum, and began a program that provided more individual instruction to students.

Wilson also tried to change the social and living conditions at the school by eliminating the elite dining clubs for upperclassmen. He wanted to establish a more democratic system in which students from all classes ate and lived together.

The proposed reform experienced resistance by some students and by some powerful Princeton alumni. Wilson, revealing a stubbornness that would mark his life in politics, refused to give in. In the end, he lost the fight and resigned as president of Princeton in 1910.

However, the publicity caused by the debate opened up a new world for Wilson. Democratic Party leaders in New Jersey approached him and persuaded him to run for governor. Because Wilson had little experience in politics, party leaders mistakenly thought that he would be easy to control.

Woodrow Wilson, shown in the center, made many improvements to the curriculum and the standards while serving as the president of Princeton University.

Governor of New Jersey

Shortly after he won the election, Wilson broke with the Democratic Party machine that had nominated him and embarked on a program of reform. He forced through the New Jersey legislature four major pieces of legislation: a direct primary act; a corrupt political practices act; a public utility control act; and a workers' compensation act.

Party leaders were stunned. They had thought that Wilson would be more cooperative. Instead, he not only broke with them, he went over their heads by appealing directly to the people for support. It was a tactic that he would later use in the White House as president.

Wilson's two years as governor brought him into the national spotlight. As the 1912 presidential election approached, many considered him to be a strong possibility for the Democratic nomination.

Woodrow Wilson

President Wilson: The New Freedom

The 1912 Democratic Convention could not decide on a nominee, and it turned to Wilson on the 46th ballot. The convention selected Governor Thomas R. Marshall of Indiana for vice president. With the Republican vote divided between Taft and Roosevelt, Wilson's election was a foregone conclusion. He won 435 electoral votes to Roosevelt's 88 and Taft's 8.

Wilson was sworn in as president on March 4, 1913, and immediately put forward a series of reforms he called the New Freedom. Reviving a practice that others previously abandoned, in 1801 he appeared personally before Congress to push for his program.

Between 1913 and 1914, Congress enacted almost all of the New Freedom reforms, which were mainly in the areas of banking, tariffs and trade, monopolies, and workers' rights.

The Federal Reserve Act of 1913 created the Federal Reserve Bank, the nation's central banking system, which regulates currency and interest rates. The Federal Reserve is still in existence today and plays a major role in the American economy.

The Underwood Tariff Act of 1913 drastically reduced tariffs. Its policy was consistent with Democratic principles and was the reverse of many Republican policies.

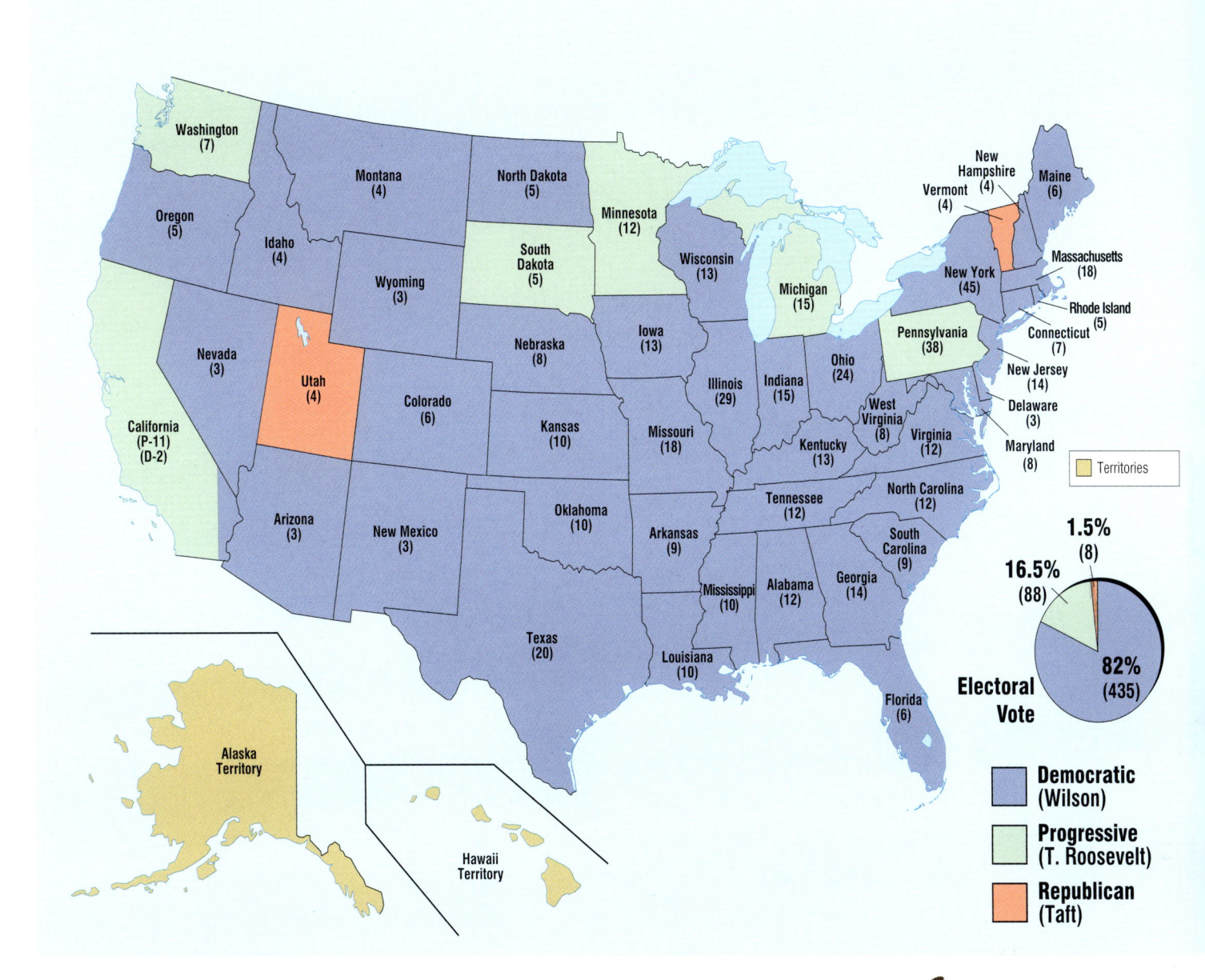

Woodrow Wilson 23

Electoral Vote
- 82% (435) Democratic (Wilson)
- 16.5% (88) Progressive (T. Roosevelt)
- 1.5% (8) Republican (Taft)

A divided Republican Party made it easy for Democrat Woodrow Wilson to win the presidential election of 1912.

Words to Know

Federal Reserve Bank (FED-ur-uhl ri-ZURV BANGK): The nation's central bank, established in 1914, which controls currency and interest rates.

New Freedom (NOO FREE-duhm): President Wilson's reform program, enacted between 1913 and 1915.

Underwood Tariff (UHN-der-wood TA-rif): A tariff passed by Congress in 1913 that dramatically reduced rates on many items.

The First Ladies

Ellen Louise Axson, the first wife of Woodrow Wilson, was born in Savannah, Georgia, where her father was a Presbyterian minister. She first met Wilson when she was a toddler and he was about six years old, but they did not meet again until they were adults. Wilson was attracted to her splendid laughing eyes and to her serene and dignified personality.

Following their marriage in 1885, they moved north as Wilson pursued his academic career. Their first child, Margaret, was born in 1886, and two other daughters, Jessie, and Eleanor, followed shortly thereafter.

Ellen Wilson was a talented artist who found time to paint despite her social obligations as the wife of a university president, governor, and then U.S. president. When the Wilsons moved into the White House in 1913, Ellen had a studio with a skylight installed so that she could continue with her art.

The First Lady received notice for her tact and grace, and she would often advise the president on certain social gestures. For example, when Wilson was eager to reach agreement with Congress on a tariff bill, Mrs. Wilson suggested inviting key lawmakers to a private dinner. They soon reached an agreement.

Upon arriving in Washington, Mrs. Wilson was shocked by the slums that housed the city's large African American population. She visited the poor in their homes and urged Congress to set aside funds to build new housing for the city's needy. The bill was pending when Ellen Wilson's health began to fail in early 1914.

As she lay dying in the White House, Congress passed the housing bill in her honor. Mrs. Wilson died on August 6, 1914. The devastated president accompanied her body back to Georgia, where he buried her alongside her ancestors.

Wilson faced a lonely future in the White House. His two youngest daughters had married in White House weddings only months before, and the president was now living alone for the first time.

Words to Know

Federal Trade Commission (FED-ur-uhl trade kuh-MISH-uhn): A body established in 1914 to monitor fair trade practices of business.

Clayton Antitrust Act (KLEYT-n an-tee-TRUHST AKT): A law passed in 1914 that gave the government more power to prosecute monopolies and trusts.

Continuing Roosevelt's policy of curbing monopolies, Wilson formed the Federal Trade Commission in 1914. Its mission was to investigate and expose businesses engaged in monopolies.

One day, late in 1914, Wilson was strolling down a White House corridor when he ran into a cousin who was taking a friend on a tour of the mansion. The friend was a 43-year-old widow named Edith Bolling Galt. Wilson took an immediate liking to her and began seeing her socially. After a brief courtship, they were married in her home in Washington on December 18, 1915.

Edith Bolling was born in Wytheville, Virginia, in 1872, the seventh of the eleven children of William and Sallie Bolling. Her father was a financially secure judge, and he sent Edith to Martha Washington College of Virginia to study music. While visiting her sister in Washington, D.C., Edith met a young man named Norman Galt, who had his own jewelry business. They were married in 1896 and lived happily in Washington, D.C., for the next 12 years. In 1908, Norman died suddenly, leaving Edith in charge of the family business.

Once she was married to the president, Edith Wilson assumed the role of First Lady. When the United States entered war in 1917, she canceled many of the routine social functions at the White House for the duration of the war. Edith Wilson saw her role as a protective one, to make sure that her husband stayed as fit as possible under the strains of the presidency. She accompanied him to Europe at the end of 1918 and remained at his side during the grueling treaty negotiations.

After Wilson became ill in 1919, Edith Wilson and the president's doctors served as a kind of buffer. Although she screened all visitors and documents directed to the president, she claimed that she made no policy decisions and did not initiate programs.

Nevertheless, the special circumstances of Wilson's illness gave her enormous power. If she was not the "first woman president," she was certainly an influential and powerful figure in government during the period between 1919 and 1921.

Wilson died in February 1924. Edith Wilson continued to live in Washington, where she became a highly respected figure in the social life of the capital. In one of her last public appearances, the 88-year-old former First Lady attended the inauguration of President John F. Kennedy in 1961. She died on December 28 of that same year, on the 105th anniversary of her famous husband's birth.

The Clayton Antitrust Act of 1914 also strengthened the government's authority to investigate the unfair practices of corporations.

A number of laws passed between 1913 and 1916 were designed to improve the conditions in which people worked. The Adamson Act, for example, established an eight hour day for railroad workers. Other laws sought to improve conditions for laborers in other industries.

Woodrow Wilson

The New Freedom was basically enacted and completed by 1915, with the passage of these laws and other minor ones. Wilson believed that his major work as president was done. The work was done at home. But far greater, and more dangerous, challenges awaited the president abroad.

Woodrow Wilson

Words to Know

dollar diplomacy (DOL-ur di-PLOH-muh-see): A U.S. policy in the Caribbean and Central America that involved protecting American business interests above all else.

President Wilson: Foreign Challenges

President Wilson was an idealist and a reformer. In 1913, he announced that he would not follow dollar diplomacy in Latin America. That is, he would not use the armed forces of the U.S. government to protect private American business interests. His first challenge came from just south of the border, in Mexico.

In 1913, following his belief in democratically elected government, Wilson refused to recognize the new revolutionary government in Mexico because it had come to power through the assassination of the previous president. In reaction to the arrest of American sailors in Mexico in 1914, Wilson sent in the U.S. Marines to occupy the city of Veracruz. The dispute was settled by arbitration among South American countries.

In 1916, turmoil within Mexico spilled over into the United States. Francisco "Pancho" Villa, a Mexican rebel, entered New Mexico and killed 17 people in the town of Columbus. Outraged, Wilson sent an army expedition, commanded by General John J. Pershing, into Mexico to search for Villa. They failed to catch the rebel and were withdrawn in February 1917.

Beginning in 1914, the president's attention was riveted on keeping America out of the war in Europe. As war broke out, Wilson suffered a great personal loss. Ellen Wilson died of kidney disease in the White House on August 6. Despite his grief, Wilson had to carry on with his duties. The president tried to keep America out of war for two more years.

Even when a German submarine torpedoed the unarmed British liner Lusitania in 1915, killing 124 Americans and more than 1,000 passengers of other nationalities, Wilson kept the United States out of the war. He proclaimed that there was such a thing as a man being too proud to fight.

In 1916, Wilson ran for reelection on the slogan "He kept us out of war." He won a narrow reelection over Republican Charles Evans Hughes, winning 277 electoral votes to Hughes's 254. The Germans refused to stop the submarine warfare against neutral nations, and Wilson's hand was eventually forced. Finally, and with great reluctance, he asked Congress on April 2, 1917, to declare war on Germany. He said in an address to Congress that the world must be made safe for democracy.

Wartime Leader

Wilson genuinely believed that World War I would be the war to end all wars. As such, he was concerned about the terms that would establish eventual peace. On January 8, 1918, the president went before Congress to outline his comprehensive peace terms, which he called the Fourteen Points. Among its proposals were self-government for different nationalities within Europe and the formation of the League of Nations, an organization of all the world's nations that would together keep the peace.

In November 1918, Germany and Austria-Hungary agreed to end the war. The power of the American forces had turned the tide against them. Wilson was so concerned about the peace treaty that he journeyed to France in December 1918 to participate in the negotiations. Accompanying him was his second wife, Edith, whom the president had married in 1915. Wilson was hailed in Paris as a hero. Adoring, weeping crowds greeted him wherever he went, and children threw rose petals in the path as he walked the streets.

Woodrow Wilson and his second wife, Edith.

28 Woodrow Wilson

Wilson settled in at the Palace of Versailles to work on the peace treaty. It took six months to write, and many considered it far from perfect, even the president himself.

But it was a beginning, and Wilson returned home to try to persuade the Senate that it should ratify the Treaty of Versailles and allow the United States to join the League of Nations.

On April 2, 1917, Woodrow Wilson addressed Congress and asked them to declare war on Germany.

The Final Campaign

Republicans, however, controlled the Senate, and many of them, including the influential Senator Henry Cabot Lodge of Massachusetts, had reservations about the treaty. These Republicans wanted the treaty worded in such a way as to indicate that the United States would not give up any of its powers if it joined the League of Nations. Republicans and even some Democrats urged the president to compromise. Wilson, however, refused to change one word of the treaty.

In order to create support for the treaty and the League of Nations, Wilson embarked on an exhausting train trip across the country in September 1919. The 62-year-old president drove himself to the limit, making speech after speech. The strain proved to be too much. While campaigning in Pueblo, Colorado, he became ill. A few days later, back in Washington, D.C., he suffered a major stroke that left him partially paralyzed.

For a month, only Mrs. Wilson and a doctor were allowed to see the president. Gradually, his doctor allowed him to resume limited activity. During this time, Edith Wilson controlled access to the president.

In order to reduce the amount of paperwork he would have to see, Mrs. Wilson wrote brief summaries of the original documents. She often guided his shaky hand when he needed to sign papers.

Woodrow Wilson and wife Edith riding in the backseat of a carriage.

Because of her role, some considered Mrs. Wilson, and some accused her, of being the acting president. In her memoirs, which she wrote years later, however, she maintained that Wilson, despite his illness, was of sound mind and in full control. Nonetheless, Wilson never did recover from the stroke and was seriously impaired during his final 16 months as president. The government, in effect, came to a grinding halt as the First Lady and the president's doctors shielded him from strenuous activity and unpleasant news.

African Americans Move North

Wartime mobilization created many new jobs in industry, especially in the northern states. During the war years, African Americans living in the South moved north in great numbers to take jobs in railroad yards, steel mills, and shipyards. They hoped to escape the poverty and discrimination that oppressed them in the South. Between 1910 and 1920, Cleveland's African American population grew by 300 percent, while Detroit's grew by more than 600 percent.

Most blacks who moved north were single young men and women in their twenties. In one of the greatest movements of population in American history, some 500,000 African Americans migrated to the North. Once there, African Americans encountered different kinds of prejudice and often faced outright violence.

In the summer of 1919, race riots rocked more than 20 cities and towns across the country. Black leaders of the time insisted on equality and an end to racial segregation, but major changes were not to come, either in the North or in the South, until the civil rights movement 40 years later.

With Wilson refusing all compromise, in 1920, the Senate rejected the Treaty of Versailles and the League of Nations. This was a bitter defeat for everything Wilson had stood for. Later that year, the Republicans won the presidential election in a landslide. In a kind of personal rebuke to Wilson and his brand of idealism, the nation sought a return to normalcy, the word coined by the successful Republican presidential candidate, Senator Warren Harding.

After the White House

Leaning on a cane, the ailing president accompanied his successor to the Capitol Building for the inauguration on March 4, 1921. While sitting in a room there, Wilson greeted fellow Democrats who came to wish him a fond farewell.

When Senator Lodge approached the president in a spirit of reconciliation, Wilson responded coldly that he had nothing further to say.

The former president and his wife retired to a house on S Street in Washington, D.C. His health continued to deteriorate, and on February 3, 1924, he died at the age of 67. Woodrow Wilson is buried in the National Cathedral in Washington, the only U.S. president to be buried in the District of Columbia.

Woodward Wilson after his stroke.

Warren Harding

In 1920, Warren Harding swept into office in a landslide election. He won more than 61 percent of the vote. The American people chose the Republican from Ohio because they were tired of the sacrifices they had to make during the war and wanted to return to peace and prosperity. Harding, a pleasant and honest man, promised "normalcy," a return to simpler, easier, normal times.

Harding soon discovered that being president had its dangers. Scandal bogged down his administration, and he came to feel betrayed by many of his closest associates. When he died after less than two and a half years in office, he had become a completely disillusioned man. Historians remember his administration today as much for its atmosphere of corruption as for its accomplishments.

Vice President Calvin Coolidge

Warren Harding

Born:
November 2, 1865
Corsica, OH

Ohio

Term:
March 4, 1921 – August 2, 1923

Party:
Republican

First Lady:
Florence Kling DeWolfe Harding

Vice President:
Calvin Coolidge

Died:
August 2, 1923
San Francisco, CA

Warren Harding

29th President of the United States

Warren Harding

Early Life

Warren Gamaliel Harding was born in Corsica, now Blooming Grove, Ohio, on November 2, 1865. He was the eldest of the eight children of George and Phoebe Harding. The family was poor and supported itself mainly by farming and occasional trading.

Young Warren spent much of his youth working on the family farm, but when his father became a partner in a village newspaper, the boy had the opportunity to teach himself typesetting. It was an interest that later blossomed into a career.

When he was 14, Warren began attending Ohio Central College in Iberia, Ohio, and he graduated in 1882. He loved to play the alto horn, and when his family moved to Marion, Ohio, Warren became the manager of the Marion Citizens' Cornet Band.

Warren worked at a number of jobs in his youth. He taught school for a year, sold insurance, and studied law on his own. But at 19, he found his profession. He enjoyed newspaper work. He landed a job on the Mirror, a town paper that supported Democratic candidates. Young Warren, however, was a Republican, and when he publicly supported the 1884 Republican presidential nominee, James G. Blaine, the newspaper fired him.

Warren Harding

Shortly thereafter, however, another town paper went bankrupt, and Harding saw an opportunity. He scraped together the $300 necessary to take over the mortgage, and at the youthful age of 19, he found himself the owner and publisher of the Marion Star.

Popular Politician

In 1891, Warren Harding married Florence Kling DeWolfe. She was an ambitious and able businesswoman who gradually took over more and more of the paper's business operations. In addition, she encouraged Harding to become more involved in politics. In 1898, he won the election to the Ohio state senate.

Harding soon gained a reputation for party loyalty and for the ability to get people to compromise.

Harding won the election as lieutenant-governor of Ohio in 1903, but an attempt in 1910 to run for governor failed. In 1914, Harding won the election to the U.S. Senate. He quickly became a highly popular senator. Harding supported the Eighteenth Amendment to the Constitution, which banned the sale of alcoholic beverages in the United States. It was also known as the Prohibition Amendment. He also supported the Nineteenth Amendment, which granted women the right to vote throughout the country.

At the end of World War I, in 1918, Harding joined the Republican majority in the Senate in voting against the Treaty of Versailles and the League of Nations. Although he would have liked to vote for the treaty, Harding felt that certain compromises in wording needed to be made, compromises that President Woodrow Wilson refused to make, thus dooming the treaty.

When the Republican National Convention opened in 1920, the party did not consider Harding as a candidate for president. The convention could not agree on a nominee, however, so a group of Republican senators advanced the name of Harding. The well-liked senator from Ohio seemed like the perfect compromise choice, and he received the nomination. The Convention selected Governor Calvin Coolidge of Massachusetts to be the vice-presidential candidate.

The Democrats nominated another Ohioan, Governor James Cox, for president. For vice president, they chose a dynamic young newcomer to politics: Franklin Delano Roosevelt of New York.

Words to Know

Eighteenth Amendment (AY- teenth uh-MEND-muhnt): An amendment to the Constitution ratified in 1919 and effective in 1920. It banned the manufacture, transportation, and sale of alcohol in the United States. It was widely ignored.

League of Nations (LEEG of NAY-shuns): An international peacekeeping organization created by the Treaty of Versailles. An idea of President Woodrow Wilson's, the League was the body that preceded the current United Nations. The U.S. Senate refused to permit the United States to become a member.

First Lady Florence Harding

Florence Kling was born in Marion, Ohio, in 1860. The daughter of Amos Kling, the richest businessman in Marion, she attended the Cincinnati Conservatory of Music. When she was 19, she eloped with a neighbor, Henry DeWolfe. They had one son, but the marriage was unhappy because of DeWolfe's heavy drinking. Florence returned with her son to Marion and divorced her husband in 1886.

Despite her father's wealth, Florence refused to live at home. Instead, she supported herself by giving piano lessons to children in the neighborhood. She and her baby lived in modest rented rooms, and she refused to accept any assistance from her family.

Florence soon met the young publisher of the Marion Star, Warren Harding. They began a courtship despite that fact that he was five years younger than she was. Over the objections of Amos Kling, the couple married in 1891.

Mrs. Harding eventually took over the management of the newspaper, thus allowing her husband more time to devote to politics. She was very supportive of his political career and at one point said, "I have only one real hobby—my husband." Harding recognized his wife's abilities and drive and nicknamed her The Duchess.

When she moved into the White House in 1921, Mrs. Harding reopened the mansion to the public. It had been closed to visitors during the war and later because of President Wilson's illness. She opened windows, and fresh flowers appeared in all the rooms. Mrs. Harding instructed the servants to pull up the shades, saying, "It's the people's house. If they want to look in, let them."

Florence Kling DeWolfe Harding

The people were tired of war and sacrifice, and they wanted a change. Harding's election seemed certain. In the first presidential election in which women had the right to vote, Harding swept the nation, winning 404 electoral votes to Cox's 127.

Another regular and much loved practice during her years in the White House was frequent garden parties held for veterans of the war.

Florence Harding was a highly popular First Lady. She took her responsibilities seriously and worked hard at the job despite increasingly poor health. In 1922, she nearly died of the effects of a chronic kidney ailment, but she recovered and resumed her duties. She was with the president when he died suddenly in August 1923, and she accompanied his body on the long train ride back to Washington, D.C., from California.

Following Harding's burial in Marion, Mrs. Harding returned to the nation's capitol, where she hoped to live. But in the following months, ill health and sorrow plagued her as a number of close friends died. Florence Harding returned to Marion in the summer of 1924 and died there on November 21.

She was 64 years old and had outlived her husband by only 15 months. Before her death, she methodically destroyed most of Harding's personal correspondence, apparently fearful that the prying eyes of future historians might damage his reputation.

President Harding

From the beginning, Warren Harding had doubts about his ability to succeed as president. Upon his election, he promised to appoint the best minds to advise him. Many of his appointments were indeed distinguished.

He selected Charles Evans Hughes as secretary of state, a former Supreme Court justice and the Republican presidential nominee in 1916. Under Hughes, the Harding administration enjoyed its one genuine success in foreign affairs. From late 1921 to early 1922, the United States sponsored the Washington Naval Conference, which wrote a treaty establishing limits on the sizes of the navies of the great powers. At the time, many people thought that the conference was a true step toward eventual disarmament and world peace.

Another distinguished cabinet appointment was Herbert Hoover, who became secretary of commerce.

Words to Know

Washington Naval Conference (WOSH-ing-tuhn NAY-vuhl KON-fur-uhnss): A conference held between 1921 and 1922 that limited the size of the navies of the great world powers.

Warren Harding

Hoover was a brilliant organizer who helped improve relations between business and the government during his eight years in the cabinet.

Some of the other of Harding's cabinet appointments were not so impressive. Harding selected Albert B. Fall, a former senator, as secretary of the interior. Fall proceeded to lead the department and the Harding administration into one of the greatest scandals in American politics. In 1922, he decided to lease government land in Wyoming known as the Teapot Dome Oil Reserve to a private oil company for development. President Wilson had set Teapot Dome aside for exclusive use by the navy.

When Fall decided to lease the lands, he did so without taking competitive bids from other companies. In addition, he accepted a $100,000 loan from an oil company for access to the Elk Hill Reserve in California. When Fall's actions became known, Congress began an investigation.

As the Teapot Dome affair unfolded, other scandals began to be uncovered in both the Justice Department and the Veterans Bureau. The Teapot Dome name, however, became a symbol for the series of government scandals.

The scandals deeply disturbed Harding. He had trusted his appointees, many of whom, he now realized, had betrayed him. As president, he had not paid close attention to the details of the presidency. He enjoyed playing poker with his friends in the White House and sipping an occasional scotch and soda, even though Prohibition banned the consumption of alcohol throughout the United States. Now, everything seemed to be coming apart.

Albert B. Fall served as a senator representing New Mexico from 1912 to 1921 and served as secretary of the interior from 1921 to 1923.

To escape the pressures of Washington, Harding embarked on a trip to Alaska in the summer of 1923. As he sailed along the Alaskan coast, he became more and more worried about the turn of events in his administration. The president, who had always suffered from high blood pressure, began to look tired and ill.

On the way back to Washington, he and Mrs. Harding visited San Francisco. On the evening of August 2, 1923, the president suffered a stroke. He died immediately.

The nation grieved over the sudden death of its president. Although scandals had been erupting around him, Harding himself had remained popular with the American people, and they mourned him deeply. His body was returned to Washington by train, and his casket was placed in the East Room of the White House for viewing. Harding was buried in Marion, Ohio, in a large mausoleum constructed with donations from the community.

The new president, Calvin Coolidge, was considered to be completely honest and free of any hint of scandal. His administration prosecuted Fall and convicted him of accepting bribes. They sentenced Fall to jail. For Harding, however, death ended the despair and sorrow that he felt once it dawned on him that his administration was a failure.

Warren Harding in Alaska, summer of 1923.

Calvin Coolidge

Calvin Coolidge was president at a time when the nation enjoyed a period of unprecedented prosperity. The New England-born president was known as Silent Cal. He was a president who said little and a man who represented the virtues of hard work and thrift. In many respects, however, the austere Coolidge seemed to embody the opposite of what the nation was experiencing.

The 1920s were a time of rapid social change: Radio became popular, women's skirts became shorter, and more and more families bought cars and traveled all over the country. Jazz became the rage, men and women danced the Charleston, and bootlegged whiskey was available practically anywhere, despite the Prohibition Amendment.

The so-called Coolidge prosperity did not touch everyone in America in the 1920s. The lives of most African Americans, rural farmers (both black and white), and many city dwellers did not improve under Coolidge.

Vice President Charles G. Dawes

Calvin Coolidge

Born:
July 4, 1872
Plymouth, VT

Vermont — Plymouth

Term:
August 3, 1923 – March 4, 1929

Party:
Republican

First Lady:
Grace Anna Goodhue Coolidge

Vice President:
Charles G. Dawes

Died:
January 5, 1933
Northampton, MA

Calvin Coolidge
30th President of the United States

Calvin Coolidge

In addition, as was later discovered, the prosperity of the period was based on unsound finances and wild speculation in the stock market. Shortly after Calvin Coolidge retired from the White House in 1929, Coolidge prosperity came crashing down on the country and led to economic collapse and depression.

Early Life

John Calvin Coolidge was born in Plymouth, Vermont, on July 4, 1872, the only son of John and Victoria Coolidge. He stopped using his first name after graduating from college. His father was a farmer and a storekeeper who dabbled occasionally in local politics. In his youth, Calvin did all of the farm chores expected of a young boy. He drove the mowing machine, tended the cattle, and planted potatoes. In the summer, he fished and enjoyed hayrides. But the death of his mother marred his happy childhood when he was only 12.

Coolidge attended Black River Academy in Ludlow, Vermont, before admittance to Amherst College in Massachusetts. After graduation in 1895, he went on to study law at a firm in Northampton, Massachusetts. While in Northampton, Coolidge began working for the local Republican Party as a volunteer. During this time, Coolidge met Grace Anna Goodhue, a teacher of the deaf. They were married in 1905 and had two sons, John and Calvin, Jr.

Calvin Coolidge poses for a picture with his wife, Grace, their two sons, and the family pet.

Calvin Coolidge

A Quiet Politician

Coolidge was not a typical politician. He rarely smiled and was often quiet and shy. Nevertheless, he was sincere and inspired the confidence of voters and other politicians. In all his years in politics, he never lost an election.

Coolidge's political career took off when he won the election for the office of mayor of Northampton in 1910. In 1912, he won the election to the Massachusetts state senate, and in 1916, he won election to be the lieutenant governor. Two years later, the voters made him governor of Massachusetts.

Coolidge achieved national recognition in 1919. That year, the police force of Boston went on strike. When the strikers became disorderly, Coolidge called out the National Guard to keep the peace, stating, "There is no right to strike against the public safety by anybody, anywhere, any time." His actions ended the police strike and made him something of a national hero.

Because of this recognition, Coolidge was a natural for the Republican vice-presidential nomination in 1920. After sweeping into office with Warren Harding, Coolidge assumed his responsibilities as vice president in his typical quiet fashion. He presided over the Senate and remained aloof from the Harding administration scandals that began to become public in 1923.

President Coolidge

Coolidge was visiting his father in Vermont in the summer of 1923 when, in the early morning hours of August 3, he received a telegram informing him that President Harding had died in San Francisco. It was 2:47 a.m., and even though Coolidge had automatically become president, he was required to take the constitutional oath of office.

After he found a copy of the oath in a book in his father's library, his father, who was a notary public, swore in Coolidge as president. A notary public is an official empowered to authorize and verify the legality of documents. In characteristic fashion, Coolidge then turned out the lights and went back to bed.

The Coolidge administration was pro-business and did everything in its power to create a positive climate for business.

President Coolidge

First Lady Grace Coolidge

Grace Goodhue was born in Burlington, Vermont, in 1879, the only child of Andrew and Lemira Goodhue. She graduated from the University of Vermont in 1902 and accepted a job as a teacher at the Clarke Institute for the Deaf in Northampton, Massachusetts.

In Northampton, she met a young lawyer named Calvin Coolidge, who was a member of the same congregational church and the same boating club. They were married at her parents' home in Vermont in 1905. A son, John, was born in 1906, and a second son, Calvin, Jr., was born in 1908.

Grace Coolidge had a warm and sunny personality, and her graciousness and openness provided a welcome contrast to her husband's shy and withdrawn personality. As he rose in politics, she performed all the social duties expected of the wife of a rising politician, and she raised a family as well.

Coolidge became president in the summer of 1923, and after the period of mourning for President Harding, Grace Coolidge began her service as Washington's principal hostess. She often entertained children, who were especially fascinated with the Coolidges' pets. In addition to their collie, Rob Roy, they kept a raccoon, named Rebecca, who lived on a diet of green shrimp and persimmons. The president, whose facial expression almost never changed, would often allow Rebecca to sit on his shoulder.

So strong was Mrs. Coolidge's sense of her responsibilities as First Lady that she carried on despite the shattering grief caused by her younger son's sudden death in 1924. When Coolidge retired in 1929, the couple moved back to Northampton to a newly purchased home called The Beeches.

However, when her husband died in 1933, Grace sold the large house and moved into a smaller one. In time, she undertook new ventures, such as her first airplane ride and her first trip to Europe. She also served as a trustee of the Clarke Institute and generally remained out of the limelight.

Grace Coolidge was one of the most popular First Ladies in history. In 1931, she was voted one of the ten greatest living women. She died at the age of 78 in 1957 and was buried next to the president in Plymouth, Vermont.

Calvin Coolidge

Coolidge did little to enforce anti-monopoly laws and even made sure that pro-business appointees filled positions on the Federal Trade Commission. When Republicans in Congress passed the McNary-Haugen Bill, which gave government subsides to farmers, Coolidge vetoed it twice. He did not believe that the government should help individuals.

Coolidge supported other measures designed to improve the economy. During his tenure in the White House, Congress passed huge tax cuts and reduced government spending by millions of dollars. The president also supported legislation to restrict immigration and extend civil-service reform.

Regarding foreign affairs, the administration's most notable achievement was the signing of the Kellogg-Briand Pact in 1928. Named in part after Coolidge's secretary of state, Frank B. Kellogg, the pact urged nations to renounce war as an instrument of international policy. However, Coolidge, like his predecessors, was not afraid to use American military power in Central and South America. He sent the U.S. Marines into Nicaragua in 1926 after civil unrest threatened American interests in that country.

President and Mrs. Coolidge stand with Secretary of Commerce Herbert Hoover and Secretary of State Frank B. Kellogg.

Calvin Coolidge

Prohibition: The Experiment That Failed

The crusade against alcohol and its effects has a long history in the United States. In 1874, the Women's Christian Temperance Union formed. Its goal was to publicize the fact that alcohol caused liver disease and other health problems.

In 1893, the Anti-Saloon League formed. This organization shifted the focus away from the individual's responsibility and sought to place blame for the ill effects of drinking on saloons. One of the most colorful opponents of saloons was a woman named Carrie Nation, who wrecked establishments with an ax.

Carrie Nation

The campaign to ban the sale and consumption of alcohol was one of the major reform movements in the United States. Reformers wanted to make life better for people. One way was to get them to stop spending their money on alcohol, which in their view, contributed to disease, poverty, and the loss of jobs.

By 1917, many political leaders supported the call for a constitutional amendment to ban the sale, manufacture, and transportation of alcohol. The new law, the Eighteenth Amendment, was ratified in January 1919 and went into effect one year later. Prohibition, however, was an experiment that failed. Most Americans wanted to drink, and soon "bootleggers" were illegally providing alcohol. Speakeasies, illegal underground bars, flourished in cities and towns. The law became unenforceable. In addition, organized crime moved into the liquor business and created an atmosphere of violence throughout the country.

Finally, in 1933, Prohibition was revoked, and Americans were allowed to drink again when the Twenty-First Amendment was ratified. The government realized that, at least in this area, it was impossible to dictate people's moral choices.

In 1924, Coolidge received the nomination for president. In the November election, he and his running mate, Charles G. Dawes of Illinois, easily defeated the Democratic ticket, which was headed by an obscure lawyer named John W. Davis. Coolidge received 382 electoral votes to Davis's 136. A third party, called the Progressives nominated Senator Robert La Follette of Wisconsin for President. He received only 13 electoral votes.

The joy of Coolidge's 1924 victory, however, was tempered by the unexpected death, earlier that summer, of his 16-year-old son Calvin, Jr. While playing tennis on the White House tennis court, the boy got a blister on his foot. It became infected, and he died within a few days. His son's death devastated Coolidge. Many observers believed that he never recovered from it. In fact, it may have played a role in his decision not to seek another term in 1928. In 1927, Coolidge issued a one-sentence statement: "I do not choose to run for president in 1928."

After the White House

In 1928, the Republicans nominated for president Coolidge's dynamic secretary of commerce, Herbert Hoover, who won the election by a landslide in November. Coolidge rode with Hoover to the latter's inauguration on March 4, 1929, and then took the train home to Northampton. He spent his retirement writing newspaper and magazine articles and publishing an autobiography.

The economic depression that descended on the United States in 1929 greatly distressed Coolidge. It seemed to be proof that his policies had failed and that more than simply a pro-business government was necessary.

While working at his desk in his study on January 5, 1933, Coolidge suffered a fatal stroke. He was only 60 years old. Coolidge was buried in Plymouth, Vermont, in the cemetery that held the graves of both his father and his son. His tombstone is the simplest grave marker of any U.S. president. It consists of a plain slab of marble with the inscription, "Calvin Coolidge: July 4, 1872 - January 5, 1933."

Calvin Coolidge shown shaking hands with Theodore Roosevelt Jr.

The Presidency in War and Peace

The men who were president in the period from 1909 to 1929—a time of peace, then war, then a return to peace—were different from each other in style and substance. Yet each represented the age in which he governed, and each left a different legacy to the nation.

Taft as President

Although marred by party strife and a disastrous defeat at the polls in 1912, William Howard Taft's policies of his one term of presidency were in many ways a continuation of those of Theodore Roosevelt's. Taft's Justice Department filed as many anti-trust and anti-monopoly suits against big business as did Roosevelt's in his last term in office. Taft also continued, on the whole, to follow the conservation policies that were set down by Roosevelt.

William Taft

Based more on friendship than politics, Roosevelt hand picked Taft to be his successor. Roosevelt later felt Taft betrayed his policies and principles.

Perhaps no one could have followed Roosevelt successfully. Roosevelt really did not want to give up office in 1909 but felt obliged to do so because of a promise he had made in 1904 not to run again. By alienating Roosevelt, Taft doomed his chances for reelection.

Taft failed, however, as a party leader, and he alienated large segments of the Republican Party by seeming to favor the Stalwarts over the Insurgents. In fact, his actual record was far less conservative, but he was unable to publicize this fact and take advantage of it. His biggest mistake, however, was angering his predecessor, the man who had made him president.

Wilson as President

In style and appearance, Wilson, who looked thin, pale, and serious, compared to Taft, always smiling, good-natured, and large, certainly contrasted each other. In terms of policies, however, Wilson's main ideas did not diverge sharply from the policies of Roosevelt and Taft.

When Wilson came into office in 1913, he had a specific agenda, the New Freedom, which was enacted almost in its entirety by 1915. Wilson focused his attention overseas, to the war raging in Europe. When the president finally, and reluctantly, led the nation into the conflict in 1917, America had reached a crossroads.

As president, Wilson now presided as commander-in-chief over an army of 4 million men. The country mobilized for war and made the sacrifices necessary for victory. After only 19 months, the war was over, but the nation changed forever. It was a traumatic time, and people were glad that the conflict had ended. They wanted life to return to normal. That is, to the way it had been before 1917.

Woodrow Wilson

The Presidency in War and Peace

During this time, from the end of the war to the end of Wilson's second term, the country did not have a functioning president. Because of a stroke he suffered in 1919, Wilson was unable to perform the full duties of president.

Wilson's stroke affected his judgment as well as his body. He became even more uncompromising and stubborn. As a result of his rigidity, he lost the two things he cared about most, the Treaty of Versailles and U.S. membership in the League of Nations.

Many today regard Wilson as a towering figure in American and world history. The map of Europe that he drew at Versailles in late 1918 and early 1919 is basically the same as the map of Europe today. One of his most cherished principles, that nationalities should govern themselves, is still widely honored.

The conflict in Bosnia, which began in the early 1990s, has a direct relationship to the policies of Woodrow Wilson, who insisted in the Treaty of Versailles that the different nationalities in the Balkans had the right to govern themselves. Of all the presidents of this period, Woodrow Wilson left the most enduring legacy.

Council of Four at the Versailles Peace Conference: Lloyd George, Vittorio Emanuele Orlando, Georges Clemenceau, and President Woodrow Wilson.

Palace of Versailles

The Age of Entertainment

During the 1920s, Americans developed a huge appetite for entertainment and recreation. By 1929, they were spending almost 4 billion dollars a year on having fun. Such games as mah-jongg (a Chinese tile game), crossword puzzles, and miniature golf became overnight crazes.

Almost every middle-class family acquired a radio, and radio helped to popularize jazz and the music of such dance fads as the Charleston. The radio also allowed most Americans to hear the voices of their political leaders for the first time.

In the 1920s, Americans also learned to love the movies. In 1922, about 40 million Americans went to the movies each week. By 1930, the number had grown to 100 million. This at a time when the population was just over 120 million and church attendance was 60 million people a week. The introduction of sound to movies with the film The Jazz Singer in 1927 added to their popularity.

Babe Ruth

Americans watched their favorite stars on the screen but also followed their personal lives with great interest. Such stars as Charlie Chaplin, Gloria Swanson, and Douglas Fairbanks captured the imagination of millions of moviegoers. When the handsome movie star Rudolph Valentino died at the age of 31 in 1926, the press turned his funeral into a media extravaganza, and crowds lined the streets for miles for the chance to view his coffin.

The 1920s were also a time when Americans turned sports figures into heroes. Baseball's main hero was Babe Ruth, who played for the New York Yankees starting in 1920. Ruth was a large man known for his off-the-field excesses in food and drink, but the public loved him anyway. He responded with such charitable works as visiting sick children in hospitals. Bill Tilden in tennis, and Bobby Jones in golf became household names as Americans indulged their passion for sports and sports figures.

Harding as President

Warren Harding's presidency began with hope and wide public support and ended 29 months later in disillusionment and death. Harding, a generous and humane man, was not suited to the country's highest office. He trusted his friends too much, and he did not pay attention to what was taking place in some departments of the government until it was too late. The greatest achievement of his administration was a naval treaty that temporarily eased international tensions.

Harding's greatest problem was that he was unable to lead. He won the election with more than 60 percent of the vote, the greatest majority victory up to that time. As such, he truly represented what the people wanted which was a return to "normalcy." But a dynamic leader would have understood that the nation could not turn back the clock.

Instead, he would have led the country forward, with vision and determination. The philosophy of the Republican Party at the time was to let business run itself and to reduce the size and impact of government as much as possible.

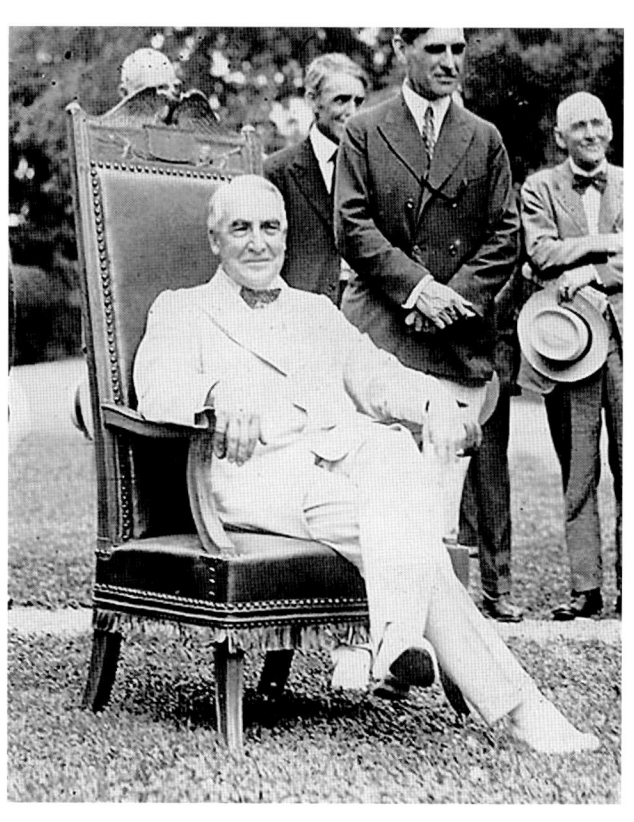

President Harding presented with a chair made from the first battleship, The Revenge.

The country, however, was too large and complex for that to be feasible. As was later discovered during the economic depression that began in 1929, the government had a great role to play in the American economy.

Following WWI, cannons and other battleship items were disposed of as scrap metals.

The Presidency in War and Peace

Coolidge as President

Calvin Coolidge was not a dynamic leader, but, unlike Harding, he was shrewd and self-protective. These traits, combined with the prosperity of the times, allowed him to enjoy a successful five and a half years as president. Like most Republicans of the day, Coolidge believed that "the business of America is business." He did very little as president, rarely working more than five hours a day and taking frequent naps.

By carefully distancing himself from the scandals of the Harding administration, Coolidge came across as an honest and frugal New Englander. Unlike Harding, who played poker and drank liquor, Coolidge was a family man who neither drank nor smoked. His clean image contributed to his popularity with the public, as did the vivacious and warm personality of his wife, Grace.

Calvin Coolidge tips his hat to a crowd.

When Coolidge walked out of the White House on March 4, 1929, people cheered him and called out, "Thank you, Mr. President." The nation was genuinely grateful for the Coolidge prosperity, although few realized that the president had done little but allow the country to prosper on its own.

Coolidge prosperity turned out to be a weak house built on a shaky foundation. Within a year after Coolidge left office, it was gone. As a result, the presidents who followed Coolidge were faced with the greatest challenges the country had ever known: The American economy collapsed, and the United States existence received threats from abroad.

Crowd at New York's American Union Bank during a bank run early in the Great Depression.

Cabinet Members

Taft

VICE PRESIDENT
James S. Sherman

SECRETARY OF STATE
Philander C. Knox

SECRETARY OF THE TREASURY
Franklin MacVeagh

SECRETARY OF WAR
Jacob M. Dickinson
Henry L. Stimson

ATTORNEY GENERAL
George W. Wickersham

POSTMASTER GENERAL
Frank H. Hitchcock

SECRETARY OF THE NAVY
George von L. Meyer

SECRETARY OF THE INTERIOR
Richard A. Ballinger
Walter L. Fisher

SECRETARY OF AGRICULTURE
James Wilson

SECRETARY OF COMMERCE
AND LABOR
Charles Nagel

Wilson

VICE PRESIDENT
Thomas R. Marshall

SECRETARY OF STATE
William J. Bryan
Robert Lansing
Bainbridge Colby

SECRETARY OF THE TREASURY
William G. McAdoo
Carter Glass
David F. Houston

SECRETARY OF WAR
Lindley M. Garrison
Newton D. Baker

ATTORNEY GENERAL
James C. McReynolds
Thomas W. Gregory
A. Mitchell Palmer

POSTMASTER GENERAL
Albert S. Burleson

SECRETARY OF THE NAVY
Josephus Daniels

SECRETARY OF THE INTERIOR
Franklin K. Lane
John B. Payne

SECRETARY OF AGRICULTURE
David F. Houston
Edwin T. Meredith

SECRETARY OF COMMERCE
William C. Redfield
Joshua W. Alexander

SECRETARY OF LABOR
William B. Wilson

Cabinet Members

Harding

VICE PRESIDENT
Calvin Coolidge

SECRETARY OF STATE
Charles E. Hughes

SECRETARY OF THE TREASURY
Andrew W. Mellon

SECRETARY OF WAR
John W. Weeks

ATTORNEY GENERAL
Harry M. Daugherty

POSTMASTER GENERAL
Will H. Hays
Hubert Work
Harry S. New

SECRETARY OF THE NAVY
Edwin Denby

SECRETARY OF THE INTERIOR
Albert B. Fall
Hubert Work

SECRETARY OF AGRICULTURE
Henry C. Wallace

SECRETARY OF COMMERCE
Herbert Hoover

SECRETARY OF LABOR
James J. Davis

Coolidge

VICE PRESIDENT
Charles G. Dawes

SECRETARY OF STATE
Charles E. Hughes
Frank B. Kellogg

SECRETARY OF THE TREASURY
Andrew W. Mellon

SECRETARY OF WAR
John W. Weeks
Dwight F. Davis

ATTORNEY GENERAL
Harry M. Daughtery
Harlan F. Stone
John G. Sargent

POSTMASTER GENERAL
Harry S. New

SECRETARY OF THE NAVY
Edwin Denby
Curtis D. Wilbur

SECRETARY OF THE INTERIOR
Hubert Work
Roy O. West

SECRETARY OF AGRICULTURE
Henry C. Wallace
Howard M. Gore
William M. Jardine

SECRETARY OF COMMERCE
Herbert Hoover
William F. Whiting

SECRETARY OF LABOR
James J. Davis

Timeline

1770

1774 — First Continental Congress

1775 — American Revolution begins

1776 — America declares independence from Great Britain

1780

1783 — Treaty of Paris formally ends American Revolution

1787 — U.S. Constitution is written

1789 — George Washington becomes president

1790

1791 — Bill of Rights becomes part of Constitution

1793 — Eli Whitney invents cotton gin

1797 — John Adams becomes president

1800

1800 — Washington, D.C., becomes permanent U.S. capital

1801 — Thomas Jefferson becomes president

1803 — Louisiana Purchase almost doubles size of the United States

1808 — Slave trade ends

1809 — James Madison becomes president

1810

1812 — War of 1812 begins

1814 — British burn Washington, D.C. War of 1812 fighting ends

1815 — Treaty of Ghent officially ends War of 1812

1817 — James Monroe becomes president

1820

1820 — Missouri Compromise is passed

1823 — Monroe Doctrine is issued

1825 — John Quincy Adams becomes president

1828 — Popular votes used for first time to help elect a president

1829 — Andrew Jackson becomes president

Timeline

1830
- **1830** Congress passes Indian Removal Act
- **1832** Samuel Morse has idea for telegraph
- **1835** Samuel Colt patents revolver
- **1837** Martin Van Buren becomes president
- **1838** Native Americans are forced to move to Oklahoma traveling Trail of Tears

1840
- **1841** William Harrison becomes president / John Tyler becomes president
- **1845** James Polk becomes president
- **1845** Texas is annexed to United States
- **1846** Mexican War begins / Boundary between Canada and United States is decided
- **1848** Gold is discovered in California / First women's rights convention is held
- **1849** Zachary Taylor becomes president

1850
- **1850** Millard Fillmore becomes president
- **1850** Compromise of 1850 is passed
- **1853** Franklin Pierce becomes president
- **1857** James Buchanan becomes president

1860
- **1860** Southern states begin to secede from Union
- **1861** Abraham Lincoln becomes president
- **1863** Abraham Lincoln gives Gettysburg Address
- **1865** Andrew Johnson becomes president
- **1865** Civil War ends / Freedman's Bureau is created / 13th Amendment abolishes slavery
- **1868** Impeachment charges are brought against President Johnson
- **1869** Ulysses S. Grant becomes president

1870
- **1873** U.S. economy collapses; depression begins
- **1876** Alexander Graham Bell invents telephone
- **1877** Rutherford Hayes becomes president
- **1879** Thomas Edison invents light bulb

1880
- **1881** James Garfield becomes president / Chester Arthur becomes president
- **1882** Chinese Exclusion Act restricts number of Chinese immigrants allowed into United States
- **1885** Grover Cleveland becomes president
- **1889** Benjamin Harrison becomes president

Timeline

1890	
1890	U.S. troops kill more than 200 Sioux and Cheyenne at Wounded Knee
1893	Grover Cleveland becomes president again
1893	Charles and J. Frank Duryea construct first car in the United States
1897	William McKinley becomes president
1898	Spanish-American War occurs
1900	
1901	Theodore Roosevelt becomes president
1903	Orville and Wilbur Wright fly their plane at Kitty Hawk, North Carolina
1908	Henry Ford produces Model T
1909	William H. Taft becomes president
1910	
1913	Woodrow Wilson becomes president
1914	Panama Canal opens
1917	America enters World War I
1919	World War I ends
1920	
1920	19th Amendment gives women right to vote
1921	Warren Harding becomes president
1923	Calvin Coolidge becomes president
1927	Charles Lindbergh makes first nonstop flight across Atlantic
1929	Herbert Hoover becomes president
1929	Stock market crashes; America enters economic depression
1930	
1933	Franklin D. Roosevelt becomes president
1939	World War II begins
1940	
1941	Pearl Harbor is bombed; America enters World War II
1945	Harry S. Truman becomes president
1945	United States drops atomic bombs on Hiroshima and Nagasaki; World War II ends. United Nations is formed

Timeline

1950	1950	Korean War begins
	1953	**Dwight Eisenhower becomes president**
	1953	Korean War ends
	1954	Supreme Court orders desegregation of schools
	1957	Soviet Union launches *Sputnik I*
	1958	United States launches *Explorer I*; NASA is created
1960	1961	**John F. Kennedy becomes president**
	1962	Cuban Missile Crisis
	1963	**Lyndon Johnson becomes president**
	1964	Civil Rights Act of 1964 is passed
	1965	First U.S. troops sent to Vietnam War
	1968	Martin Luther King, Jr. is assassinated
	1969	**Richard Nixon becomes president**
	1969	Neil Armstrong is first person to walk on moon
1970	1970	First Earth Day is celebrated
	1973	OPEC places oil embargo resulting in fuel shortages
	1974	Nixon is first president to resign
	1974	**Gerald Ford becomes president**
	1975	War in Vietnam ends
	1976	America celebrates its bicentennial
	1977	**Jimmy Carter becomes president**
	1978	Leaders of Israel and Egypt sign the Camp David Accords
	1979	U.S. embassy in Iran is attacked and hostages are taken
1980	1981	**Ronald Reagan becomes president**
	1981	American hostages are released; Reagan appoints first woman to Supreme Court, Sandra Day O'Connor
	1986	U.S. space shuttle *Challenger* explodes after lift-off
	1989	**George H. W. Bush becomes president**
1990	1991	Persian Gulf War occurs
	1992	U.S. troops are sent to Somalia to lead multinational relief force; Riots explode in Los Angeles
	1993	**William J. Clinton becomes president**
	1993	World Trade Center is bombed by terrorists
	1995	Bomb destroys federal building in Oklahoma City
	1998	U.S. bombs Iraq; Impeachment charges are brought against President Clinton
	1999	First balanced budget in 30 years is passed; Impeachment trial ends
2000	2000	Clinton sets aside land for national parks and monuments; Outcome of the presidential race is clouded due to voting miscounts
	2001	**George W. Bush becomes president**
	2001	Terrorist Attack on the World Trade Center; President Bush announces War on Terrorism
	2002	No Child Left Behind Act is signed into law
	2003	U.S. troops are sent to Iraq
	2009	**Barack Obama becomes president**

Presidents of the United States

President	Birth	Party	Term	Death
George Washington	February 22, 1732; Westmoreland Cty., VA	None	April 30, 1789 - March 4, 1797	December 14, 1799; Mt. Vernon, VA
John Adams	October 30, 1735; Braintree (Quincy), MA	Federalist	March 4, 1797 - March 4, 1801	July 4, 1826; Quincy, MA
Thomas Jefferson	April 13, 1743; Abermarle Cty., VA	Democratic-Republican	March 4, 1801 - March 4, 1809	July 4, 1826; Charlottesville, VA
James Madison	March 16, 1751; Port Conway, VA	Democratic-Republican	March 4, 1809 - March 4, 1817	June 28, 1836; Orange County, VA
James Monroe	April 28, 1758; Westmoreland Cty., VA	Democratic-Republican	March 4, 1817 - March 4, 1825	July 4, 1831; New York, NY
John Quincy Adams	July 11, 1767; Braintree (Quincy), MA	Democratic-Republican	March 4, 1825 - March 4, 1829	February 23, 1848; Washington, D.C
Andrew Jackson	March 15, 1767; Waxhaw, SC	Democratic	March 4, 1829 - March 4, 1837	June 8, 1845; Nashville, TN
Martin Van Buren	December 5, 1782; Kinderhook, NY	Democratic	March 4, 1837 - March 4, 1841	July 24, 1862; Kinderhook, NY
William Henry Harrison	February 9, 1773; Berkeley, VA	Whig	March 4, 1841 - April 4, 1841	April 4, 1841; Washington, D.C.
John Tyler	March 29, 1790; Charles City Cty., VA	Whig	April 4, 1841 - March 4, 1845	January 18, 1862; Richmond, VA
James Polk	November 2, 1795; Mecklenburg Cty., NC	Democratic	March 4, 1845 - March 4, 1849	June 15, 1849; Nashville, TN
Zachary Taylor	November 24, 1784; Orange Cty., VA	Whig	March 4, 1849 - July 9, 1850	July 9, 1850; Washington, D.C.
Millard Fillmore	January 7, 1800; Locke Township, NY	Whig	July 9, 1850 - March 4, 1853	March 8, 1874; Buffalo, NY
Franklin Pierce	November 23, 1804; Hillsborough, NH	Democratic	March 4, 1853 - March 4, 1857	October 8, 1869; Concord, NH
James Buchanan	April 23, 1791; Cove Gap, PA	Democratic	March 4, 1857 - March 4, 1861	June 1, 1868; Lancaster, PA
Abraham Lincoln	February 12, 1809; Hardin Cty., KY	Republican	March 4, 1861 - April 15, 1865	April 15, 1865; Washington, D.C.
Andrew Johnson	December 29, 1808; Raleigh, NC	Republican	April 15, 1865 - March 4, 1869	July 31, 1875; Carter County, TN
Ulysses S. Grant	April 27, 1822; Point Pleasant, OH	Republican	March 4, 1869 - March 4, 1877	July 23, 1885; Mount McGregor, NY
Rutherford B. Hayes	October 4, 1822; Delaware, OH	Republican	March 4, 1877 - March 4, 1881	January 17, 1893; Fremont, OH
James Garfield	November 18, 1831; Orange, OH	Republican	March 4, 1881 - September 19, 1881	September 19, 1881; Elberon, NJ
Chester Arthur	October 5, 1830; North Fairfield, VT	Republican	September 20, 1881 - March 4, 1885	November 18, 1886; New York, NY
Grover Cleveland	March 18, 1837; Caldwell, NJ	Democratic	March 4, 1885 - March 4, 1889; March 4, 1893 - March 4, 1897	June 24, 1908; Princeton, NJ

Presidents of the United States

President	Birth	Party	Term	Death
Benjamin Harrison	August 20, 1833; North Bend, OH	Republican	March 4, 1889 - March 4, 1893	March 13, 1901; Indianapolis, IN
William McKinley	January 29, 1843; Niles OH	Republican	March 4, 1897 - September 14, 1901	September 14, 1901; Buffalo, NY
Theodore Roosevelt	October 27, 1858; New York, NY	Republican	September 14, 1901 - March 4, 1909	January 6, 1919; Oyster Bay, NY
William H. Taft	September 15, 1857; Cincinnati, OH	Republican	March 4, 1909 - March 4, 1913	March 8, 1930; Washington, D.C.
Woodrow Wilson	December 28, 1856; Staunton, VA	Democratic	March 4, 1913 - March 4, 1921	February 3, 1924; Washington, D.C.
Warren Harding	November 2, 1865; Corsica, OH	Republican	March 4, 1921 - August 2, 1923	August 2, 1923; San Francisco, CA
Calvin Coolidge	July 4, 1872; Plymouth, VT	Republican	August 3, 1923 - March 4, 1929	January 5, 1933; Northampton, MA
Herbert Hoover	August 10, 1874; West Branch, IA	Republican	March 4, 1929 - March 4, 1933	October 20, 1964; New York, NY
Franklin D. Roosevelt	January 30, 1882; Hyde Park, NY	Democratic	March 4, 1933 - April 12, 1945	April 12, 1945; Warm Springs, GA
Harry S. Truman	May 8, 1884; Lamar, MO	Democratic	April 12, 1945 - January 20, 1953	December 26, 1972; Kansas City, MO
Dwight Eisenhower	October 14, 1890; Denison, TX	Republican	January 20, 1953 - January 20, 1961	March 28, 1969; Washington, D.C.
John F. Kennedy	May 29, 1917; Brookline, MA	Democratic	January 20, 1961 - November 22, 1963	November 22, 1963; Dallas, TX
Lyndon Johnson	August 27, 1908; Stonewall, TX	Democratic	November 22, 1963 - January 20, 1969	January 22, 1973; San Antonio, TX
Richard Nixon	January 9, 1913; Yorba Linda, CA	Republican	January 20, 1969 - August 9, 1974	April 22, 1994; New York, NY
Gerald Ford	July 14, 1913; Omaha, NE	Republican	August 9, 1974 - January 20, 1977	December 26, 2006; Rancho Mirage, CA
Jimmy Carter	October 1, 1924; Plains, GA	Democratic	January 20, 1977 - January 20, 1981	
Ronald Reagan	February 6, 1911; Tampico, IL	Republican	January 20, 1981 - January 20, 1989	June 5, 2004; Bel Air, CA
George H. W. Bush	June 12, 1924; Milton, MA	Republican	January 20, 1989 - January 20, 1993	
William J. Clinton	August 19, 1946; Hope, AR	Democratic	January 20, 1993 - January 20, 2001	
George W. Bush	July 6, 1946; New Haven, CT	Republican	January 20, 2001 - January 20, 2009	
Barack Obama	August 4, 1961 Honolulu, Hawaii	Democratic	January 20, 2009 -	

Index

A

Adamson Act, 25,
African Americans, 7, 30,40
Allied powers, 7,
Arlington National Cemetery, 17
Army, U.S., 7, 49
Arthur, Chester A., 12, 57, 60
automobile(s), 9

B

Balkans, 50
Ballinger, Richard, 16, 54
Blaine, James G., 34
Blatch, Harriet Stanton, 8
Bosnia, 50
Bryan, William J., 14, 54
Bull Moose Party, 6, 17
business(es), 6, 9, 14, 24-26, 35, 38, 43, 46, 48, 52, 53

C

cabinet, 10, 12, 16, 37, 38, 54
Charleston, 40, 51
civil liberties, 9
Civil Rights Movement, 30
civil-service reform, 45
Civil War, 20, 57
Clayton Antitrust Act, 24, 25
Congress, U.S., 6, 16, 18, 20, 22, 24, 27, 28, 38, 45, 56, 57
Coolidge, Calvin, 9, 32, 35, 39-47, 53, 55, 58, 61
    born, 40, 42, 61
    died, 40, 47, 61
    First Lady, 40, 44
    term, 40, 61
    vice president, 55, 61
Coolidge, Calvin Jr., 47
Coolidge, Grace Anna Goodhue, 40, 44
Coolidge, John Calvin, 42
Cox, James, 35, 36

D

Davis, John W., 46, 55
Dawes, Charles G., 46, 55, 40
Democratic Party, 21, 22
Depression, U.S. economic, 42, 47, 52, 53, 57, 58

DeWolfe, Henry, 36
dollar diplomacy, 26

E

economy, 21, 22, 45, 52, 53, 57
Eighteenth Amendment, 46, 35
elections, presidential,
    of 1908, 14, 15
    of 1912, 6, 10, 17, 22, 23, 48
    of 1916, 27, 37
    of 1920, 9, 17, 32, 35, 43
    of 1924, 46, 47
electoral, 14, 17, 22, 23, 27, 36, 46
    map, 23
    vote(s), 6, 8
Elk Hill Reserve, 38

F

Fall, Albert B., 38, 55
farmers, 14, 40, 45
Federal Reserve Act (1913), 22
Federal Reserve Bank, 22, 23
Federal Trade Commission, 24, 45
foreign affairs, 6, 18, 37, 45
France, 7, 27

G

Galt, Norman, 25
Germany, 6, 7, 27, 28
Grant, Ulysses S., 12, 57, 60

H

Harding, Florence Kling DeWolfe, 33, 36, 37, 39
Harding, Warren, 9, 17, 31-39, 43, 44, 52, 53, 55, 58, 61
    born, 33, 34, 61
    died, 33, 39, 61
    First Lady, 33, 36, 37
    term, 33, 61
    vice president, 33, 55
Hayes, Rutherford B., 15, 57, 60
Hoover, Herbert, 37, 38, 45, 47, 55, 58, 61
Hughes, Charles Evans, 55, 27, 37

I

immigration, 45
Insurgents, 14, 16, 49

J

jazz, 40, 51
Justice Department, 38, 48

K

Kellogg-Briand Pact (1928), 45
Kellogg, Frank B., 45, 55
Kennedy, John F., 17, 25, 59, 61

L

La Follette, Robert, 46,
Latin America, 26
League of Nations, 18, 27-29, 31, 35, 50
Lodge, Henry Cabot, 29
Lusitania, 27

M

Marines, U.S., 26, 45
Marion, Ohio, 34, 36, 39
Marshall, Thomas R., 18, 22, 54
McKinley, Wiliam, 13, 15, 58, 61
McNary-Haugen Bill, 45
Mexico, 26
monopolies, 4, 6, 22, 24
movies, 51

N

Nation, Carrie, 46
national banking system, 6
National Guard, 43
national park system, 4, 16
Navy, U.S., 4, 38
New Freedom reforms, 22
Nicaragua, 45
Nineteenth Amendment, 8, 35

O

organized crime, 46

Index

P
Payne-Aldrich Tariff, 16
Pershing, John J., 26
Philippine Commission, 13
Pinchot, Gifford, 16
presidency, 9, 16, 18, 25, 38, 48, 49, 50-53
Progressive Party, 6, 17
Prohibition, 9, 35, 38, 40, 46

R
radio(s), 9, 40, 51
railroad workers, 25
reforms, 6, 14, 21, 22
Republican Party, 6, 14, 16, 17, 23, 42, 49, 52
Roosevelt, Franklin Delano, 35, 58, 61
Roosevelt, Theodore, 4-6, 10, 13, 14, 16, 17, 23, 24, 47-49, 58, 61
Root, Elihu, 13
Ruth, Babe, 51

S
Senate, U.S., 28, 29, 31, 35, 43
Sherman, James S., 10, 14, 54
solicitor general, U.S., 13
Soviet Union, 7, 59
Spanish-American War, 13, 58
speakeasies, 9, 46
Stalwarts, 14, 49
Stanton, Elizabeth Cady, 8
stock market, 42, 58
suffrage movement, 8
Supreme Court, U.S., 10, 13, 17, 37, 59

T
Taft, Helen "Nellie" Herron, 12
Taft, William H., 4, 6, 11-17, 22, 23, 48, 49, 54, 58, 61
   born, 11, 12, 61
   died, 11, 61, 17
   First Lady, 11, 12, 15
   term, 11, 61
   vice president, 11, 54
tariffs, 14, 16, 22
Teapot Dome Oil Reserve, 38
Treaty of Versailles, 28, 31, 35, 50
trusts, 14, 24
Twenty-First Amendment, 46

U
Underwood Tariff Act (1913), 22, 23
United Nations, 35, 58

V
Valentino, Rudolph, 51
Veterans Bureau, 38
Villa, Francisco "Pancho", 26

W
Washington D.C., 12, 17, 25, 29, 31, 37, 56, 60
Washington Naval Conference, 37
White House, 4, 9, 10, 15, 17, 18, 22, 24, 25, 27, 31, 36-39, 42, 45, 47, 53
Wilson, Edith, 18, 25, 27
Wilson, Ellen Louise Axson, 18, 20, 24
Wilson, Woodrow, 6, 17-31, 35, 36, 38, 49, 50, 54, 58, 61
   born, 18, 20, 61
   died, 18, 31, 61
   First Lady, 18, 20, 24, 25, 27
   term, 18, 61
   vice president, 18, 54
Wisconsin, 23, 46
World War I, 6-8, 18, 27, 35, 58
Wyoming, 23, 38

Further Reading

Bausum, Ann. *Our Country's Presidents*. National Geographic Children's Books, 2009.

Hammond. *Hammond's Book of the Presidents*. Hammond World Atlas Corporation, 2009.

Johnson, Pamela. *...If You Lived When Women Won Their Rights*. Scholastic, Inc., 2008.

Maupin, Melissa. *William Howard Taft*. The Child's World Inc., 2008.

McNeese, Tim. *The Progressive Movement: Advocating Social Change*. Facts on File, Inc., 2007.

Otfinoski, Steven. *Calvin Coolidge*. Marshall Cavendish Inc., 2008.

Pastan, Amy. *Eyewitness First Ladies*. DK Publishing, Inc., 2008.

Souter, Gerry and Janet. *Warren G. Harding*. The Child's World Inc., 2008.

Streissguth, Thomas. *The Roaring Twenties*. Facts on File, Inc., 2007.

Sullivan, George. *Mr. President: A Book of U.S. Presidents*. Scholastic Inc., 2009.

Venezia, Mike. *Woodrow Wilson: The Twenty-Eighth President*. Children's Press (CT), 2007.

Websites to Visit

www.enchantedlearning.com/history/us/pres/list.shtml

www.whitehouse.gov/kids

http://pbskids.org/wayback

www.kidsinfo.com/American_History/Presidents.html